LITTLE IMPERFECTIONS

A TALL TALE OF GROWING UP DIFFERENT

A GINGER WITH A SOUL BOOK

Published by Ginger With A Soul LLC in partnership with RBS Projects LLC

PO Box 13524, Los Angeles, CA 90013

ISBN: 979-8-9862836-2-3

LITTLE IMPERFECTIONS

A TALL TALE OF GROWING UP DIFFERENT

BY PEET MONTZINGO AND ROCKWELL SANDS

Not all babies are born the way you think

When your mom and dad are little, things aren't always in sync

I came out "normal," if there was ever such a thing

I was more than half their size
     by the time of my first spring!

It was hard for my mom to be a parent
when she couldn't hold me much

and though she wouldn't
          ever dare it...

                    ...she thought of giving up.

I didn't realize I was different growing up
I thought every house was full of tiny things

Until my first day of kindergarten
The other parents were
SO TALL...

...much more than mine, it seemed.

Other kids would laugh and point
When my mom would drop me off
That's how I learned that I was different

But kept telling myself,
"You're not!"

My siblings would get the easy chores
and I was always in the middle

of helping out
around the
house

wishing

I was

little

My brother bragged that he was man of the house
But let's be honest... it was me

And every time we'd play sports together
He'd force me to play on my knees

But the more they were with us, the more they would see
that we were pretty much normal, as normal as can be

We watched movies, fought, and talked all night
The only thing that made us different

was my family's line of sight

Their parents would always say,

"Make yourself at home!"

But I felt so lost!

I was used to things being low

Sometimes when things seem perfect, it never really was
and when I was eleven,
my mom and dad split up

My mom had her hands full raising two boys and a girl
while my dad found a new wife, and got lost inside her world
My stepmom was average height, must be why we didn't get along
But since I didn't see them much, I never tried to right the wrongs

I had to find an outlet
for what I was feeling

So I turned to music...
it helped to start the healing

In my mom's new house
my brother and I shared a room

We slept in bunks against a wall
we painted blue

His lungs didn't work right,
it was hard for him
to breathe

So in the night
I'd climb over
his stools and oxygen machine

Dwarfism isn't just about being shorter than the rest

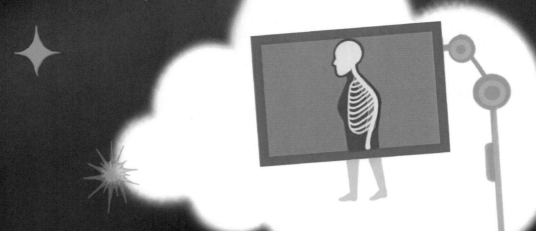

When my brother was born,
his spine was shaped like an "S"

My sister's legs are full of metal rods

and we spent our life savings on a
scooter for my mom

My dad's whole back is lined with nails and screws

and when my brother was a kid, nurses often called "code blue"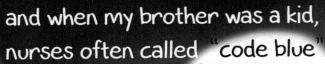

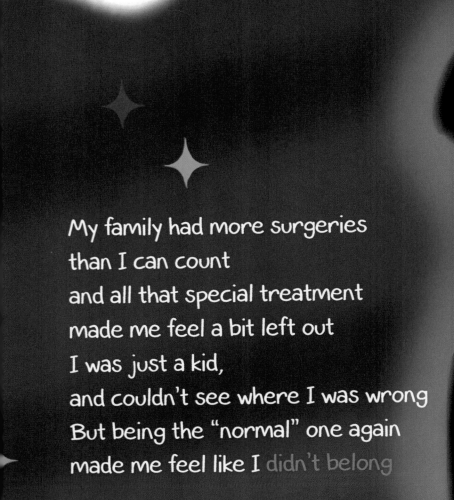

My family had more surgeries
than I can count
and all that special treatment
made me feel a bit left out
I was just a kid,
and couldn't see where I was wrong
But being the "normal" one again
made me feel like I didn't belong

School was tough for me, I couldn't ever focus
I'd fail tests, couldn't listen, and my teachers all would notice
My mom asked the doctor what was going on with me
The doctor sat us down, and said I had ADHD
I already was too big for my mom to keep up
and my diagnosis made raising me more tough
But she told me we all grow in our own ways

"Your brain is just a little different,
and that's okay!"

By the time I got to high school,
I was even taller

I started acting out
which made my family feel smaller

Holidays at our house were always magic times
like taking family photos around the Christmas lights
In my second year of high school, we were kings of Halloween
We both dressed up as different men of mystery

But in my bed at night,
I remembered nothing lasts forever
I would think about my dad
and missed the times we were all together

My dad leaving hit me
harder than I would admit
It made me feel numb...
another way I
didn't fit

To make things worse,
I couldn't drive when I turned sixteen
With special driver's pedals,
how could my mom teach me?

But through all the ups and downs,
music was always there

I sang in the car, and played trombone in first chair

I taught myself piano and how to make home movies

and for the first time in life, I felt I really knew me

My whole life,
I felt like I was meant for something else
I guess you could say I was searching for myself

So when I finished school
and needed a change
I hugged my whole family
and hopped on a plane

With a head full of hope,
I didn't know where to start
How do you show the world
                    your heart?

But I knew I loved laughter,
and how people can be moved

And somehow I knew
    that was what
        I wanted
            to do

I learned to take comfort
in the little things I need
like sleeping with a fan that sounds like
my brother's old oxygen machine

I still like putting coffee mugs
in the bottom cabinets
I still see myself as little,
though people can't imagine it

All these things remind me
I didn't grow up like most kids
But I grew to find my strength
in what I thought were weaknesses

Sometimes it's easy to wish you could change

If you're **big**
or you're little,
or people look at you strange

The truth is, being different is something to treasure
We are all different, and in this together

So if you're reading this, no matter where you are
No matter who you love, and no matter what you're not
You don't have to be perfect to be beautiful, too

Because the little imperfections are what add up to
YOU!

Want to experience the book in a different way?

Scan the barcode below to watch the
full video version of LITTLE IMPERFECTIONS!

Featuring the familiar faces you know and love!

AUTHOR'S NOTE

SHEEEESH... If you would've told me 2 years ago that I was going to write a children's book, I would've laughed. Rockwell and I never dreamed of becoming children's book authors, but somewhere along all the ups and downs we went through to create the book you're holding now, it became one of the most amazing experiences of our lives... and we wouldn't change a thing.

Bringing LITTLE IMPERFECTIONS to life was a true labor of love. I don't like to sound cringey with all the "thank you's," but I do want to give the spotlight to Rockwell for helping me bring my vision for this entire project into the world... from the words you just read to the video adaptation of LITTLE IMPERFECTIONS, including the original music we independently and exclusively made for it. My family obviously played an enormous role in this project as well—Mom, Dad, Jen and Andrew. I'm going to be honest. This was a hard story to tell. Mostly because so much of it involved my family and their insecurities, hardships, and vulnerability. There were hard conversations I had with them about the events that were told in this book and its loose truths based on my life, yet they still supported me and understood its bigger purpose: to remind YOU that no matter how old you are, no matter how you look, no matter where you come from, we all feel a little bit different, and that's okay... because we believe the very things that make us different are the things that make us beautiful.

Reading this book always reminds me of that. And my only hope is that our message helps you and your loved ones to unapologetically love and embrace yourselves. Even if you, dear reader, are the one person it helps, then I've accomplished what I set out to do. I can't tell you how much it means that my story is now, in some way, a "little" part of yours.

Love always,

Peet ☺

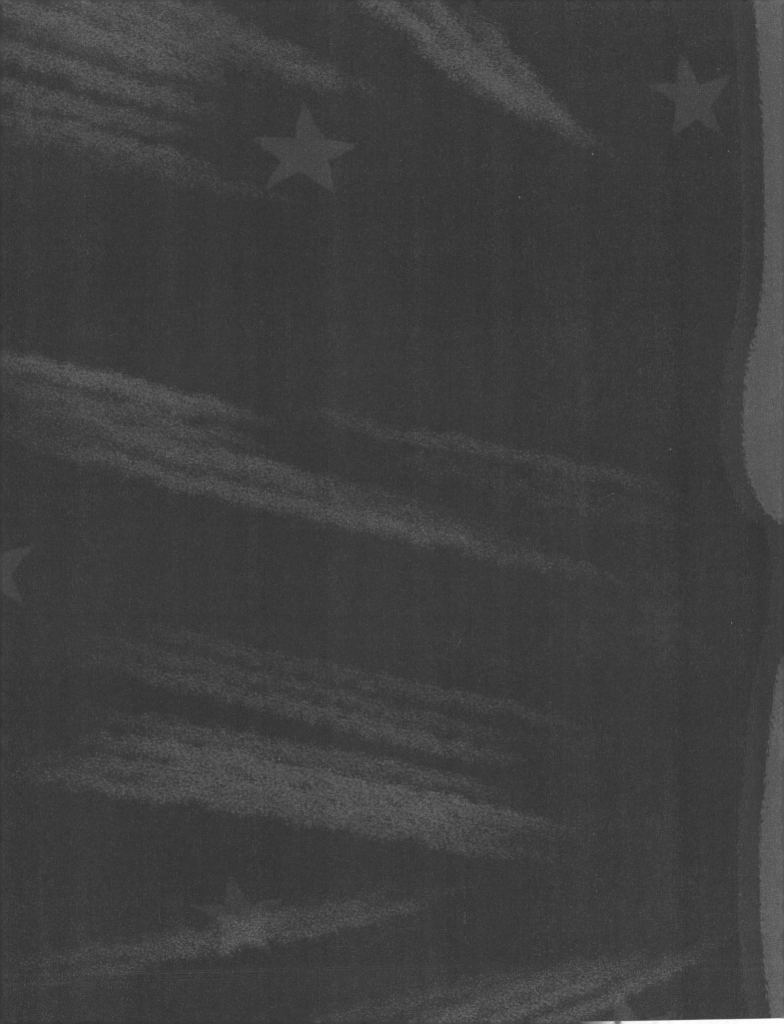

PEET MONTZINGO

is a multi-faceted artist with a curious and kind heart, whose talents span creating original content, singing, comedy, and so much more. Through his fascination with the local mysteries of his neighborhood to his deep bond with his mother and family, Peet skyrocketed to internet fame, boasting millions of followers who find themselves deeply engaged and supportive of his endeavors. Peet often raises awareness for dwarfism with a lighthearted and charming presence, shining a loving light on his mother and siblings, all of whom are little people.

ROCKWELL SANDS

is an author, musician, and entrepreneur. On top of composing the original score for the visual portion of Little Imperfections alongside Peet, he has written songs that have received worldwide radio airplay and have been featured in several forms of media, from Netflix original series to car commercials. Rockwell lives in Brooklyn and has been close friends with Peet for over ten years.

Published by
Ginger With A Soul LLC
in partnership with RBS Projects LLC